The Hamlyn Book of Early Man

Josef Kleibl
Edited by Anthony P. Harvey and Don Tills
Illustrated by Zdeněk Burian

Hamlyn
London • New York • Sydney • Toronto

Designed and produced by Artia for
The Hamlyn Publishing Group Limited
London ● New York ● Sydney ● Toronto
Astronaut House, Feltham, Middlesex, England
© Artia 1975
© this edition The Hamlyn Publishing Group Limited 1976
Illustrations © 1975 by Prof. Zdeněk Burian
ISBN 0 600 37095 X
Printed in Czechoslovakia
1/11/01/51

Contents

Glossary

Aegyptopithecus (p.13) An early ape which lived 28—30 million years ago and whose remains have been found at Fayum, Egypt.

Anthropology The study of the physical and social history of man.

Australopithecus (southern ape, pp.16—21) A group of early hominids which lived from more than 5 million years ago to under 1 million years ago. *Australopithecus africanus* (southern ape of Africa, p.16) was the smallest, *Australopithecus robustus* (robust southern ape, p.18) was slightly larger; it is sometimes called *Paranthropus robustus*. The largest of the australopithecines was *Australopithecus boisei* (pp.20—21); this was originally called *Zinjanthropus*. Their remains have been discovered mainly in Africa although there is evidence to suggest that they also lived in the Far East. Some authorities regard *Homo habilis* (handy man, pp.22—23) as being in reality *Australopithecus habilis*.

Cro-Magnon man (p.44) A type of *Homo sapiens sapiens* who is named after the site of the discovery near Les Eyzies in the Dordogne region of France. He lived about 30,000 to 20,000 years ago.

Dental arcade The shape and position of teeth within the jaw.

Dryopithecines (p.12) A group of early fossil apes which include the ancestors of the chimpanzee, gorilla and the line of descent leading to man. *Proconsul africanus* which lived about 19 million years ago is a dryopithecine.

Evolution The development of complex forms from more simple ones.

Fetish An object which is thought to have magical powers or which represents a god.

Fossil The remains of prehistoric life, either plant or animal. The term also includes traces of activity, such as petrified footprints.

Gigantopithecus (p.15) The largest primate known; it was 3 metres tall and weighed 300 kilos. It originally lived in China and India.

Hominoidea, hominidae Hominoidea is the name given to the group of animals which includes the gibbons, siamangs, apes and the family of man. Hominidae is the scientific name given to the family of man which includes the australopithecines, *Homo erectus* and *Homo sapiens*.

Homo erectus (erect man, p.24) The name given to several groups of men originally living in Asia, Africa and Europe from over 2 million years ago until about 200,000 years ago. These include *Homo erectus modjokertensis* (p.26), *Homo erectus erectus* (Java man, p.24) and *Homo erectus pekinensis* (Peking man, pp.30—31).

Homo habilis see *Australopithecus*

Homo sapiens (modern man, p.32) This group includes man of today *Homo sapiens sapiens* (p.44), as well as *Homo sapiens steinheimensis* (Steinheim man, pp.32—33), *Homo sapiens neanderthalensis* (Neanderthal man, p.38).

Ice age A name commonly given to the last 2 million years, during which time there have been four periods when the ice sheets and glaciers have advanced over the land and sea.

Java man see *Homo erectus*

Living floors Preserved areas of human activity.

Matriarchy A society in which the female is dominant and in which the descent is traced through the mother.

Meganthropus palaeojavanicus (giant old-Java man, p.26). First found in 1941 in Java, this is regarded by some as an ancestor of *Homo erectus erectus* and by others as an australopithecine.

Neanderthal man see *Homo sapiens*

Olduvai Gorge (p.21) Located on the Serengeti Plain of Tanzania, Africa, this gorge is famous for the number of specimens of fossil man which have been found by the Leakey family.

Oreopithecus (p.15) Originally nicknamed 'the abominable coalman', the remains of this fossil ape have been found in the brown coal (lignite) deposits of Italy. It is about 10 million years old.

Palaeontology The study of fossils.

Paranthropus see *Australopithecus*

Peking Man see *Homo erectus*

Pliopithecus An ancestor of the gibbons which lived 12—15 million years ago.

Primates A division within the mammals that includes animals which have the following characteristics: eyes which look to the front and which can see in depth, an ability to grasp objects, and flat nails instead of claws.

Proconsul africanus see Dryopithecines

Propliopithecus This may be the ancestor of *Aegyptopithecus* and is probably about 32 million years old.

Quadruped A mammal which walks on four feet.

Ramapithecus (pp.14—15) A possible ancestor of the australopithecines whose remains have been found in Africa and India. It lived between 12 and 14 million years ago.

Steppes The grasslands of Eurasia. The present-day steppes extend across the southern part of the USSR and into Siberia.

Stratum A layer of rock.

Taiga The belt of coniferous forest which stretches across the USSR and which is also found in North America. To the north of the taiga is the tundra.

Tundra The area to the north of the taiga. The temperature is below freezing point for most of the time and the soil below about 30 cm is permanently frozen.

Zinjanthropus see *Australopithecus*.

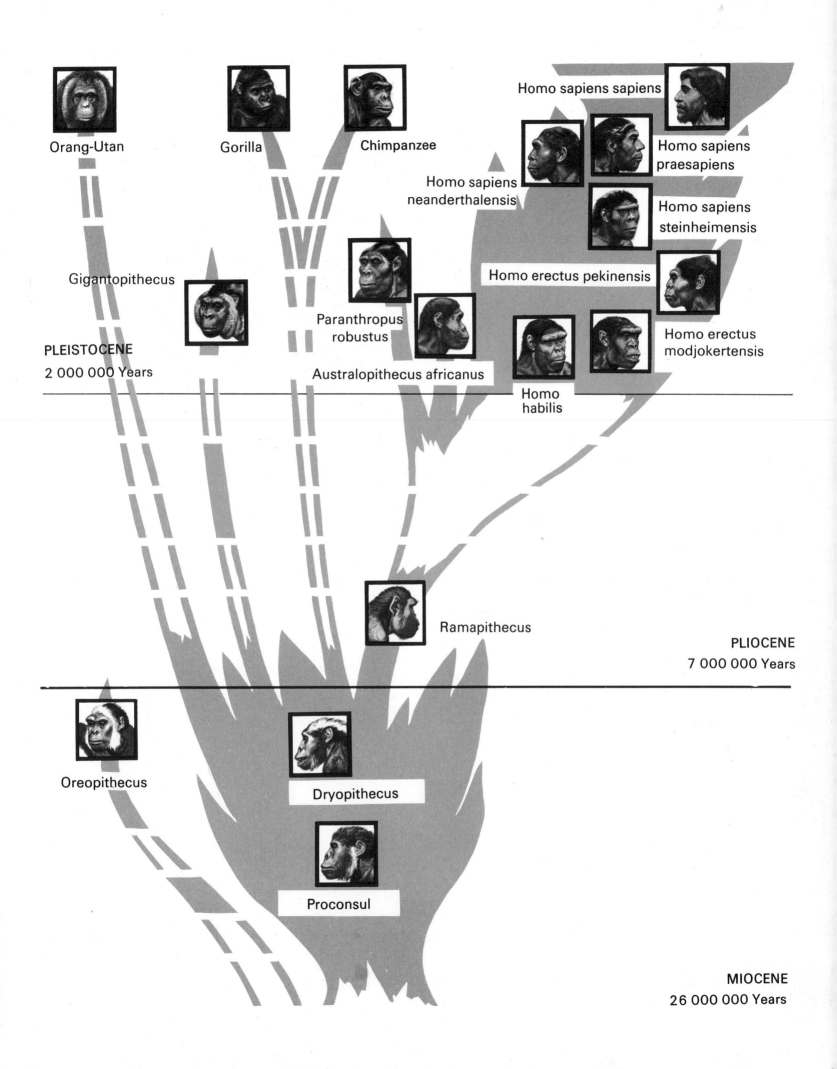

Orang-Utan

Gorilla

Chimpanzee

Homo sapiens sapiens

Homo sapiens
praesapiens

Homo sapiens
neanderthalensis

Homo sapiens
steinheimensis

Gigantopithecus

Homo erectus pekinensis

Paranthropus
robustus

Homo erectus
modjokertensis

PLEISTOCENE

2 000 000 Years

Australopithecus africanus

Homo
habilis

Ramapithecus

PLIOCENE

7 000 000 Years

Oreopithecus

Dryopithecus

Proconsul

MIOCENE

26 000 000 Years

Introduction

Man is unique in the animal world. He alone can exercise control over his environment. This ability to change and adapt his surroundings for his own use has been a feature of man's activity for countless years. Over thousands of years, in South America and the Far East, terraces have been constructed on the gently sloping valley sides to provide more land for crops. Dam making too has been carried out over a similar span of time. It is strange therefore that it was not until the mid-nineteenth century that the idea of man in a fossil form, and hence very ancient, began to even be considered.

The argument over prehistoric man raged for years. Religious prejudice and ignorance had led people to believe that man was created in his present form.

The discovery and exploration of the more remote areas of the world quickly led to more and more finds of prehistoric man. Fossils of land animals are by no means common and therefore the chances of finding fossils of man are remote. When an animal dies the flesh is quickly eaten by scavengers. The bones are scattered by the wind and rain.

It is fortunate that early man used caves as his home for these provide a good environment for the preservation of the remains. Another favourite place for early man's camp was by a lake-side. The changes in water level, and hence the sediments deposited, provide another ideal site for the preservation of prehistoric man and his cultures.

To be able to unravel the story of man's evolution it is necessary to find many specimens. It was, however, the initial discovery of a relatively large number of fossils of man in a localised area — western Europe — which clouded scientists' thoughts and predictions on human evolution.

The study of man's evolution requires at least a limited knowledge of why and how animals are named and classified. Every living creature is placed into one of the two great kingdoms, plants and animals. Within the animal kingdom the next major division is based on the existence of a backbone. Those animals *without* a backbone are called invertebrates, and those with chordates. Man has a backbone, therefore he is a chordate. Within the chordates there are other sub-divisions. Man is warm-blooded, has hair, suckles his young, and has two sets of teeth during his lifetime. These characteristics place man in the group of animals called mammals. In the opening section of this book we shall see that man also exhibits the features of a group of animals within the mammalian class which are called primates.

Those animals which have a number of the same features as man are grouped together as a family called Hominidae. This family includes prehistoric man as well as the living forms.

Each animal or plant is given two, or sometimes three, Latin names. The most common ones given refer to the genus and species. The characteristic of a species is that all the members must be able to interbreed successfully and their offspring must be fertile. Working out the relationships of the different animals is like constructing a complicated family tree. Man's place within the animal kingdom is:

KINGDOM	Animalia
PHYLUM	Chordata
CLASS	Mammalia
ORDER	Primates
FAMILY	Hominidae
GENUS	*Homo*
SPECIES	*sapiens*
SUB-SPECIES	*sapiens*

Modern man's scientific name is therefore *Homo sapiens sapiens*.

The story of the development of man is gradually becoming clearer although there are still many gaps in our knowledge. The following pages describe and illustrate the various types of prehistoric man and their ancestors, as well as giving an insight into their customs and everyday life.

For a long time the countryside behind the white mountain has afforded hospitality to this tribe of prehistoric men. In its forests and plains they knew every animal trail as well as every brook with clear water. Now it all belongs to the past for the tribe is moving away to find new hunting ground. Perhaps these men wonder whether there will be more animals in their new surroundings and how long their journey will take. They do not know anything about time; they do not realise that their journey is a part of continuous travel that hundreds and thousands of similar tribes have undertaken and others will have to undertake in their endless search through vast continents and countless years. One day scientists — palaeontologists and anthropologists — will follow their trail, searching, finding, losing and recovering again the traces of life in the distant past.

Left: The excavation of a site yields various findings in each layer of the earth and reads like a book to a scientist. Every layer resembles a page and each page contains information about its origin and age. On many pages there is no mention of prehistoric man but on others there is evidence of his way of life. The deeper the scientists go through this book the older the information they find.

EVOLUTION OF THE APES

Life on Earth originated 3,200 million years ago. The first simple animals and plants evolved slowly in to the forms of today. Many creatures, for example, the dinosaurs, have been extinct for millions of years. Man belongs to a group of animals called primates, which also includes lemurs, monkeys and apes. Primates have eyes which look to the front and have the ability to see in depth. They can grasp objects and have flat nails instead of claws.

To understand how man has evolved it is necessary to trace the evolution of the primates and especially the hominoids. This group includes the gibbons, siamangs, apes (orang-utan, chimpanzee and gorilla) and man. The oldest primate fossils are 70 million years old. Important fossil primates have been found in Egypt, including *Aegyptopithecus* in 1964. One of the most interesting fossil primates is *Proconsul africanus*. It lived about 19 million years ago and is named after a chimpanzee called Consul who once lived at the London Zoo. This animal is a member of a group called dryopithecines which includes the ancestors of the chimpanzee, gorilla, and the line leading to man.

Above: *Aegyptopithecus zeuxis* lived some 28—30 million years ago. It is a much earlier form than *Proconsul* and is the oldest of the dryopithecines so far found. It had a small brain and a long dog-like face. The hands and feet were typical of a tree-living quadruped. It also possessed a short tail. The fossilised remains of *Aegyptopithecus* were found at Fayum in Egypt. This region is a treasurehouse of primate fossils. *Propliopithecus,* also found there, may even be an ancestor of *Aegyptopithecus*.

Below: The Fayum is now a desert region and palaeontologists had to work in stifling heat to extract the valuable fossils. When *Aegyptopithecus* lived the area was one of tropical forests.

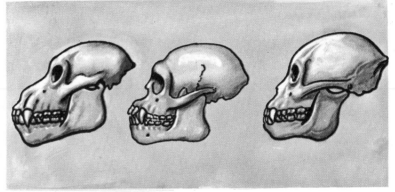

Above: From the fragments found palaeontologists are able to make reconstructions of these ancient animals. The three skulls are those of: left to right, *Aegyptopithecus, Pliopithecus* and *Proconsul*. The large canine teeth were probably used in defence. The gradual shortening of the face is clearly shown.

Left: A lower jaw of a typical dryopithecine shows the thickness of the jaw and the arrangement of the teeth.

Below: The map shows the major sites where the various forms of dryopithecines have been found. From this it can be seen that they were widely distributed.

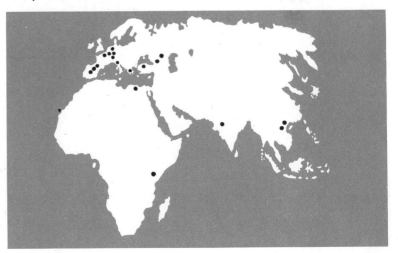

APE INTO MAN

Early this century fossil jaw fragments of a primate were discovered in the Siwalik Hills of India. Over the years the pieces were examined by various scientists until finally in the early 1960s they were all thought to be from the same type of animal, called *Ramapithecus*. Similar remains have now been discovered in Kenya. All the specimens are between 12 and 14 million years old. Because they are so fragmentary it has been difficult to interpret the features of *Ramapithecus*.

Dentally it is a member of the family which includes man, for the canine teeth are small, the dental arcade rounded and the face flatter than that of an ape.

Whether or not *Ramapithecus* could walk erect will not be solved until more specimens are discovered. It is generally believed to be an ancestor of the australo-pithecines (p.16) and therefore it must be more than 16 million years since the split in the evolutionary line leading to the present-day apes and man.

Above: The fossils of *Oreopithecus* were found in a brown coal mine in Italy. It was similar in size to a chimpanzee but a tree dweller. *Oreopithecus,* nicknamed the abominable coalman, is probably an evolutionary dead-end.

Above: *Gigantopithecus* is also an evolutionary dead-end. It is the largest known primate being 3 m. tall and weighing nearly 300 kilograms. Fossils of *Gigantopithecus* have been found in China and India.

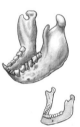

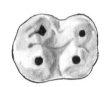

Above: This diagram shows the dental arcade of the upper jaw of a gorilla, chimpanzee, *Ramapithecus,* and modern man. The rounding of the arcade and the reduction in the size of the canine teeth is clearly shown. It is also noticeable how close the shape of the jaw of *Ramapithecus* is to man.

Left: The jaws of *Gigantopithecus* and man.

Right: One of the methods which palaeontologists have used to distinguish apes from the prehistoric forerunners of man is known as the Y-fissure. With apes, the molars, or grinding teeth, of the jaw have four small points or cusps; with man and his ancestors there are five cusps divided by a Y-shaped fissure.

Below: Groups of *Ramapithecus* would wander on the edges of the lush tropical forest. They gathered seeds and plants for food.

THE MISSING LINK

There is a very large gap in our knowledge of how evolution took place between *Ramapithecus,* who lived 12—14 million years ago, and the first australopithecines which have been dated as about 5 million years old. It is known, however, that from almost the earliest times there were a number of different types of these early hominids. Four species are recognized: *Australopithecus africanus, Australopithecus habilis, Australopithecus robustus* and *Australopithecus boisei.* Some experts put the third and fourth of these in a separate genus called *Paranthropus* while another group regard *habilis* as a member of the same genus as man himself and call it *Homo habilis.* Some authorities think that *africanus* evolved gradually into *habilis.* The smallest of the australopithecines was *africanus* while *robustus,* as the name suggests, was more heavily built. *Boisei* is the largest of them all.

The first australopithecine fossils were found in South Africa but in recent years the richest finds have been in East Africa, in Olduvai Gorge, Lake Rudolf and near the Omo River.

Australopithecus africanus walked erect, although perhaps not as well as modern man. The teeth are hominid, the canine ones being the same size as our own. The brain was initially small, not more than 400 cubic cm.

Africanus was a plains dweller living by the side of rivers. He lived in small groups. At night the whole group might have taken to the trees to sleep in relative safety. Caves were also probably used as protection against the weather and wild animals.

Above: Weaker and slower than many of the wild animals, the australopithecines often had to make do with small game. Sometimes they would make off with scraps from the spoils of a larger beast, especially if it was away at a water-hole. The tools used were primitive and mainly consisted of objects which could be picked up and used at once. This primitive armoury included sticks, stones and rocks, and animal bones.

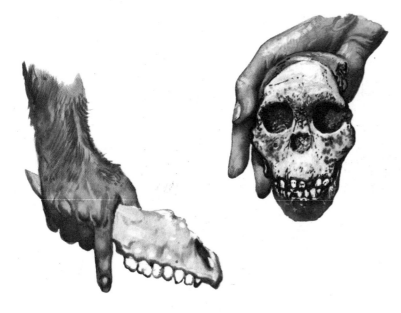

Above: The first australopithecine fossil was discovered by Professor R. Dart in 1925 in a limestone quarry at Taung in Botswana. Dart called his find Taung child as the skull appeared to be that of a five to six year old child with milk teeth still present. This skull triggered off an uproar, the majority of scientists claiming that it was a man-like ape and therefore not in the direct line of human ancestry.

Above: Remains of the animals eaten by *africanus* have been found with his fossilised bones. These bones show signs of having been intentionally broken to obtain the marrow. Stones would have been used to break open the bones.

THE ROBUST SOUTHERN APE

Remains of *Australopithecus robustus* have been found only in South Africa, at Kromdraai and Swartkrans. It was named *robustus* simply because it is slightly larger than *africanus*. The latter form was approximately 1.4 m. tall and weighed between 30 and 40 kilos, while *robustus* was over 1.5 m. tall and tipped the scales at over 45 kilos. However, *robustus* may have possibly reached 60—70 kilos.

Robustus certainly walked upright, but he was not such an able walker as *africanus*. The larger jaws and teeth indicate a vegetarian diet. Although both *africanus* and *robustus* may well have had a common ancestor the former continued to evolve while the latter was doomed to extinction about 1 million years ago.

Above: Because of his vegetarian diet it is probable that *Australopithecus robustus* would have lived in bush country or on the edge of the forests. Here he would have had a wide choice of fruits and roots.

Left: The original finds of the australopithecines were made in South Africa in limestone quarries and caves. This material is very hard and makes the extraction of the fossils difficult. One famous palaeontologist, Dr Broom, even used explosives to excavate. The late Dr L.S.B. Leakey found extremely rich fossil bearing rocks in Olduvai Gorge (page 21). These were much easier to work and the extraction of the valuable fossil finds was easier. Other areas rich in the fossilised ancestors of man are now being excavated and they include the Omo River area in Ethiopia and the Lake Rudolf site in Tanzania. Lake Rudolf promises to be one of the most exciting and useful sites so far found. No doubt more sites will be discovered in this part of Africa.

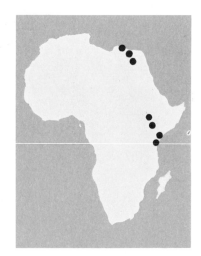

Above: The map shows the main sites where the fossils of australopithecines have been found. The new areas in East Africa have provided specimens which show that australopithecines are at least 5 million years old. As more information is gained it may prove that the 'cradle of mankind' is in East Africa. The climate of this region is now dry and arid but it was milder in the time of early man. In spite of this, life must have been very precarious as the average age of death was probably about eighteen, although a few individuals lived to the ripe old age of forty.

19

AUSTRALOPITHECUS BOISEI

(Zinjanthropus)

When Dr L.S.B. Leakey made this find in the rocks of Olduvai Gorge he was so overjoyed that he called the specimen 'Dear Boy'. It was first named *Zinjanthropus boisei*. The name *boisei* is derived from the Boise Fund which provided the Leakey family with financial support for their work. The new fossil was 1¾ million years old. Specimens have since been found at Omo more than 3¾ million years old.

The teeth of *boisei* were larger than those of *robustus* and the jaws more powerful. These would require very strong chewing muscles which would have been attached to a large crest on the top of the skull. This indicates that *boisei* was mainly a vegetarian and almost certainly one who fed on very coarse plant matter. Not in the main line of human evolution *boisei*, like *robustus*, died out about 1 million years ago.

A river has cut a gorge some 90 m. deep through a succession of lake and volcanic deposits. The gorge is nearly 50 km. long and varies in width from some 25 m. to several hundred metres. It is from the walls of the gorge, sloping gently in parts and sheer in others, that the fossils have been, and are being, excavated. There are five beds: Bed 1 at the bottom is the oldest and Bed 5 at the top is the youngest; Beds 2 and 4 are composed of former lake and river sediments, showing that the region has been under water at various times in the past. The middle of Bed 1 has been dated at about 1¾ million years old and the upper part of Bed 2 at about 1 million years. Beds 3 and 4 are, of course, more recent. Remains of *boisei* have been found in Bed 1 and up to the middle of Bed 2. Olduvai has given us some living floors. These are the remains of a site occupied by man. They were covered in volcanic ash and lava so preserving the tools used by man, and bones of the animals which were killed. These living floors have been found in Beds 1 and 2.

Above: *Australopithecus robustus* (left); *Australopithecus boisei* (centre); *Australopithecus africanus* (right). The close relationship between *robustus* and *boisei* is clear.

Above: Although the evidence from the teeth, jaw and skull of *boisei* suggests that he was predominantly a vegetarian we cannot be certain of this. Even if he did not hunt animals he may have collected birds' eggs or have eaten grubs and other insects. The chimpanzee has often been observed catching and eating termites. Also, we cannot be sure that he did not use tools, as stone implements have been found in Olduvai Gorge. It is important to realise, too, that just because he was not a hunter it does not mean that tools were not made and used for other purposes.

21

THE FIRST MAN?

eater and so a hunter of other animals.

There is a large difference in the brain size between the 400 cubic cm. of *africanus* and the estimated 650 cubic cm. of *habilis*.

This increase is very significant as it is the first sign of the rapid development that was about to occur in the brain. If a date of 1½ to 2 million years is accepted for *habilis,* the following figures for brain capacity are obtained: *Ramapithecus* 300 cubic cm., *Australopithecus africanus* 400 cubic cm., *Australopithecus habilis* 650 cubic cm., and modern man 1,300 cubic cm. So between about 14—4 million years the brain size increased by 100 cubic cm., from 4—2 million years by 250 cubic cm. and in the last 2 million years by 650 cubic cm. Why was it that the brain developed so fast? One of the most vital steps was the change from walking on four feet to walking on two. This freed the hands for the use of tools and for carrying. The more the brain was used in the manipulation of the hands the more rapid became its development. The anatomy of the foot, ankle and knee joints of *habilis* show that he walked with his knees bent.

Dr Leakey had originally found a number of primitive stone tools at Olduvai which for sometime were considered to have been used by *boisei*. However, when the remains of *habilis* were found in the same layer of rock it was immediately clear that here was the most likely maker and user of the tools.

In 1964 a new fossil hominid was described in a scientific paper. This specimen was discovered at Olduvai by Dr Leakey and although very similar to *africanus* showed some more advanced features as well. Leakey and his fellow workers named this new discovery *Homo habilis* (handy man), so placing it in the same genus as modern man. However, further work has convinced many scientists that *habilis* is closer to the australopithecines than it is to *Homo*.

The first finds consisted of teeth and a jaw. These were very similar to *africanus,* although slightly smaller. The small teeth, human-like canines, slimmer jaws and no crest on the top of the skull imply that he lived on a mixed diet and did not require the large powerful chewing jaws of *robustus* and *boisei*. It can therefore be reasonably assumed that *habilis* was a meat

Above: With his increasing intelligence *habilis* may have been able to stalk small animals and catch them unawares, or even kill larger ones already wounded by other predators.

Above: Selected stones were chipped and worked to give sharp edges and points for cutting and scraping.

Left: As the stone tools found with *habilis* were not of an advanced type — no arrow heads or hand axes — his main weapon was almost certainly a heavy stick or club. Large animals, unless injured, would have been too swift or strong for him to hunt. However, he could easily have killed slow moving animals.

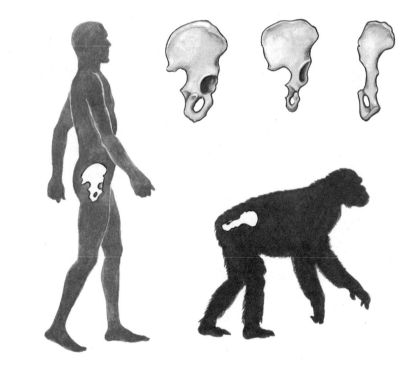

Above: Pelvis of modern man (left); *Australopithecus* (centre); and chimpanzee (right). It can be seen from the picture that there has been a progressive change in the shape of the hip bone to enable man to achieve his unique method of two-limbed movement. Man's hip blades have become smaller and shaped like a 'basket'; the spine has taken on an S-shaped curve. The foot has altered from a grasping instrument to a specialised piece of equipment for passing the weight of the body to the ground and transmitting the power involved in walking. The leg bones have adapted to allow for full extension of the knee and hip joints.

EARLY MAN IN THE FAR EAST

The earliest years in the development of man have been studied from fossils which have been found in Africa. For the next stage of development it is necessary to examine and study specimens from the Far East. For many years these finds of prehistoric man were thought to be of completely different types and popular names given to them include Peking man and Java man. Today all of the finds are regarded as subspecies of *Homo erectus* (erect man) and they are between 300,000 and 1 million years old.

These men of the Far East show great advances over the australopithecines. Brain size has increased to at least 750 cubic cm. and various estimates up to over 1,000 cubic cm. have been made for individual specimens. In size these men were similar to modern man and changes in the shape of the skull and teeth also show an intermediate stage between the australopithecines and present-day man. During this major stage of man's development he learnt to communicate and language may even have developed. His other great achievement was in the use of fire.

One of the earliest fossil men found was Java man. Scientists first called him *Pithecanthropus erectus* which means erect ape-man. He is now called *Homo erectus erectus*. The first find was made in 1891 by Eugene Dubois, a Dutch army doctor. The remains of the skeleton found in Java showed that this man stood upright and reached a height of 160—165 cms. He had a strongly built skull with powerful, well developed brow-ridges over the eyes. The teeth no longer show any basic difference from those of modern man.

The first specimens came from the gravels of the Solo River, at Trinil in Java. Although another expedition was mounted to visit the Trinil site no more remains were discovered, in spite of the removal of 1,640 cu.m. of earth. It was to be over forty years before more fossils of Java man were found. In 1936 the geologist G.H.R. von Koenigswald discovered fragments on the slopes of Sangiran Hill, a spot 64 kms from Trinil.

Above: Eugène Dubois was at one time commissioned to survey the rocks of Java and became determined to discover fossils which proved man's animal origins.

Above: Dubois pored over maps, crossed the length and breadth of the jungle and then, as if led by instinct, stopped and excavated on the edge of the River Solo, at Trinil, in Java.

Right: Java man wandered from place to place, gathering fruit and various tubers and roots. He made stone tools to help in hunting and for cutting up any game caught. It is clear from the remains of plants which were found in the same layer of rock as Java man that he lived in a tropical forest. At the same time elephants, rhinoceroses, antelopes and various deer were abundant, for the fossilised bones of these animals were also found at the same site. Dubois thought that all the animals perished at the same time during a volcanic eruption. The site does lie at the foot of the active volcano Lawu-Kukusan. The torrential rains would have carried their bodies into the valley together with the soil deposited by the flooded River Solo. Here they were destined to remain for more than 700,000 years. Dubois actually found a skull, teeth, and a complete thigh bone. The thigh bone shows signs of disease and is therefore the earliest example we have of disease in man.

Above: The memorial stone at Trinil, marking the spot where Java man was discovered.

Above: Ernest Haeckel (left) who supported Charles Darwin's theory of the origin of man and the finder of the proof, Eugène Dubois.

25

FOSSIL MEN OF JAVA

As well as the specimens which undoubtedly belong to *Homo erectus erectus* other specimens have been found on Java which are not so easy to classify but are very important. In 1936 Professor von Koenigswald found at Modjokerto, on the Solo River, the skull of a young child.

This specimen is incomplete, lacking almost all of the face and the back of the skull. The important thing is that it comes from rocks which are much older than those in which the original finds of Java man were made although it is undoubtedly a juvenile Java man.

Other finds which have been made in these rocks are of massive jaw fragments containing very large teeth. The original fossil was found in 1941 by von Koenigswald who called it *Meganthropus palaeojavanicus* (giant old-Java man). Some have suggested that these are fragments of Java man, others that they are the remains of an australopithecine.

Above: The plains and tropical forests, which the small groups of *Homo erectus* crossed in their search for food, hid many dangers. Often they would be overcome by the wild beasts which attacked them. Even if these first men were armed and more intelligent than their forebears, they found themselves defenceless against a large number of beasts of prey. One of their most feared enemies was the sabre-toothed cat.

Below: Although Java man's stone tools were only made in a crude and primitive manner he did deliberately shape rocks and stones. One side was normally smooth and the other was worked only in places. Java man could remember the best way of working stone and this was passed on from generation to generation, leading to better and more efficient tools.

THE FIRST MEN IN EUROPE

Homo erectus did not live only in the Far East. His remains have been found in Europe and Africa. Finds have been made in Africa by Dr Leakey in Olduvai Gorge, while others of a similar age have been found at Ternifine in Algeria. Further discoveries have been made at Casablanca and Rabat. All of this material has strong similarities to the Peking finds (p.30).

The most famous European specimen of *Homo erectus* is the jaw found in Germany. At the beginning of this century Professor Schoetensack had an arrangement with the owner of a sand pit at Mauer, six miles south of Heidelberg, to see all the prehistoric bones discovered during quarrying. It was in this way that Professor Schoetensack received in 1907 a huge jawbone, which was very old and well preserved. Its characteristics were its massive form and its powerful teeth, which matched the teeth of modern man. It was only later that this jaw could be compared with the discoveries in the Far East. Although more massive than the finds in China, the jaw has many similarities to them and it certainly belongs to *Homo erectus.*

There have been other finds of erect man in Europe. In a cave in Greece the very well preserved Petralona skull was found. Another find in 1965 at Verteszöllös in Hungary is thought by some to represent a form between *Homo erectus* and *Homo sapiens.* There is also evidence to suggest that the men at Verteszöllös whose scientific name is *Homo erectus* (seu *sapiens*) *palaeohungaricus* used fire.

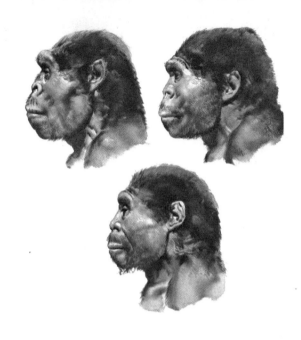

Above: At about the same period as Java man was living, tribes of Heidelberg man were living in the Neckar area of Germany. The climate there was warmer than it is today. The region was lightly covered with mixed forest and woods of oak trees, and also with areas of thick bush which alternated with grassy prairies. Herds of prehistoric elephant wandered, as well as wild horses, elk and other animals. Beavers built their lodges in the streams. But even Heidelberg man was unable to move around without risk. He had to tackle wild animals, amongst them the sinister sabre-toothed cat.

Below: At the time when Heidelberg man was living both males and females would have helped to gather food for the tribe. Children may also have been encouraged to help from their youngest days. Catching fish and other river creatures would have been one good way to learn the skills of hunting. When successful, no doubt they felt the same pleasure as the adults.

Above: These reconstructions represent: top left, the find at Modjokerto in Java. It shows strong brow ridges and receding chin. The specimen is thought to be about 1 million years old. Top right is *Homo erectus erectus* with more prominent features in skull shape and a greater cranial capacity. The age of this specimen is about 700,000 years old. The bottom reconstruction is of *Homo erectus pekinensis,* the youngest and most advanced of the *Homo erectus* group. He lived about 300,000 to 500,000 years ago. The shape of his jaw has a more modern appearance and brain size has again increased. These three reconstructions are certainly pointers to the evolution of man.

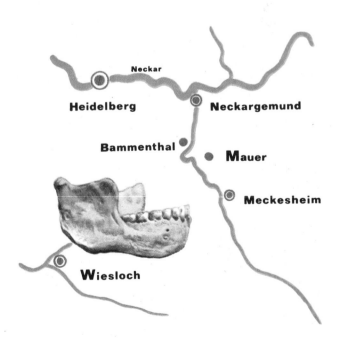

Above: A map showing where the Heidelberg jaw was discovered at Mauer. It was found in a sand pit. The sands are the old bed of the River Neckar. As well as the jaw the sands are very rich in other fossils, such as land and fresh-water molluscs and mammals.

29

PEKING MAN

According to Chinese tradition the world was created by giant birds of prey. When they later returned to the Earth they had made, they arrived during a period of storms. Often unable to fly away again because of the heavy rain they died and their bones were soon buried. This legend was still widely believed by the people living in the village of Chou-k'ou-tien, near Peking, when they discovered the bones of various prehistoric animals in nearby rocks and caves.

From 1927—1937 palaeontologists discovered in this area the remains of nearly forty-five individuals, which were later to be called *Homo erectus pekinensis* or erect Peking man. These men were far more advanced than those found by Dubois on Java. The ave-

rage size of the skull was already 1,050 cubic cm. Their height was between 155 and 160 cm. From the same strata the wealth of their culture was also discovered. It consisted of a number of implements hewn from quartz, and tools worked from sandstone, flint and limestone. They lived in the area for a very long time. Countless generations must have looked out from the top of the small hill over the plain of Khei-pei which was teeming with game. They hunted in groups and it was in doing this that they doubtless came to communicate with each other. Their language was one of signals. Peking man had developed the feeling that he was different from the other animals around him.

Above: One of the greatest surprises in the excavation at Chou-k'ou-tien was the discovery of a fire-place in the cave. It is the oldest fire-place in the world. Here was definite proof that these men knew the uses of fire. Man's use of fire, and his mastery of it, is one of the most important acts in his entire history. Fire gave heat in the cold cave, offered protection against the wild animals, and provided a means of cooking food.

Below: Most of the time Peking man would hunt deer, antelope, and wild horses, which they may have driven over the edges of cliffs.

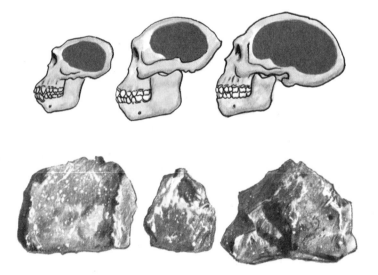

Above: The skull of a chimpanzee (left), *Australopithecus* (centre), and *Homo erectus pekinensis* (right). Over millions of years the size of the brain has increased greatly. Once man acquired the ability to think in abstract terms and understand how one thing can cause another, the manufacture of tools for specific jobs would proceed rapidly. *Australopithecus habilis* (p.22) was probably the first to cross this threshold but *Homo erectus* took yet another important step along the road towards humanity as we know it.

THE COMING OF MODERN MAN

Various fragments provide tantalizing clues to man's evolution. Little is really known, however, of the evolutionary stages between *Homo erectus* and *Homo sapiens* (modern man).

In 1933 D. Berckhemer, who was curator of the Stuttgart Natural History Museum in Germany, discovered a skull at Steinheim, about twenty miles north of Stuttgart. By studying the remains of other skulls, discovered in England and France, it was possible to build up a picture of Steinheim man. Here was a man with a narrow but comparatively high skull, whose forehead was more domed than that of *Homo erectus* even if the brow ridges were more like those of Peking man. This skull is in fact nearer to that of modern man, in the rounded shape at the back, its vertical appearance, and in other respects.

From Swanscombe on the River Thames in Kent have come remains of a similar creature. Both show many of the characteristics of modern man and are classed in the group *Homo sapiens*. Some consider these to be the ancestors of a later group called Neanderthal man (p.38).

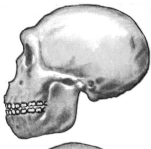

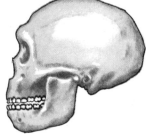

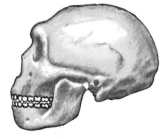

Above: The *Homo sapiens* found at Steinheim lived in the mild climate of an interglacial period. In the wooded countryside there were elephant, wild deer and bears. He was already aware of many aspects of the world around him — the way that night followed day, seasons, storms, thunder and lightening, rainbows — but it was up to his descendants thousands of years later to explain them.

Above: Reconstructions of the skulls of, from top to bottom, *Homo sapiens steinheimensis* (Steinheim man), the progressive and the classic; and *Homo sapiens neanderthalensis*.

Left: No-one really knows what was eaten during these times but certainly plants, including roots, seeds and fruits would have been on the menu. Steinheim man would also have hunted, most likely taking the smaller game but also willing to tackle elephant, rhinoceros, buffalo and other large animals. The meat would not be eaten raw but cooked over the fire.

Below: Fire was nature's most magnificent and precious gift. It was far from easy to make it. Once a group had managed to get a fire going they would not allow it to go out. It would be carried from place to place during the hunting expeditions. If it was lost then it would be recovered only by a chance finding of a natural fire.

THE AGES OF ICE

In quite recent times northern Europe was almost completely covered by ice. Great ice sheets and rivers of ice, called glaciers, swept over the hills and plains, grinding even the hardest rocks, smashing and pounding stones into pebbles and finally dust. The ice did not advance once but four times. Such periods are called glacials. During the intervening times the climate was often warmer in northern Europe than it is today. These periods are appropriately known as interglacials.

further afield, for freezing winds blew across central and south-western Europe. Not only did the ice cover the north of Europe but the glaciers of the Alps flowed down their valleys, and in Asia, America and New Zealand glaciers and ice sheets were advancing. The ice of the Antarctic spread further northwards than today.

The last ice age occupied most of the last 2 million years and it was only about 10,000 years ago that it finally retreated from Scandinavia. Apart from the

Today about 15 million square km. of the Earth's surface is covered by ice, but during the ice age about twice this area would have been affected. A vast white desert covered the whole of northern Europe. In the south and east the front of the ice reached the River Volga and stretched along the northern edge of Czechoslovakia to the Harz Mountains of Germany. It ran along the lower reaches of the Rhine and across southern England. The presence of the ice was felt much

effect on climate the ice locked up large quantities of water which resulted in the sea level being much lower than it is at present. The direct result of this was the creation of land bridges. Asia was united with America across the Bering Strait. Many of the islands of Indonesia were joined to the mainland. Offshore islands, such as Britain, were joined with the neighbouring continental masses. The climatic changes and the land bridges affected the spread of man.

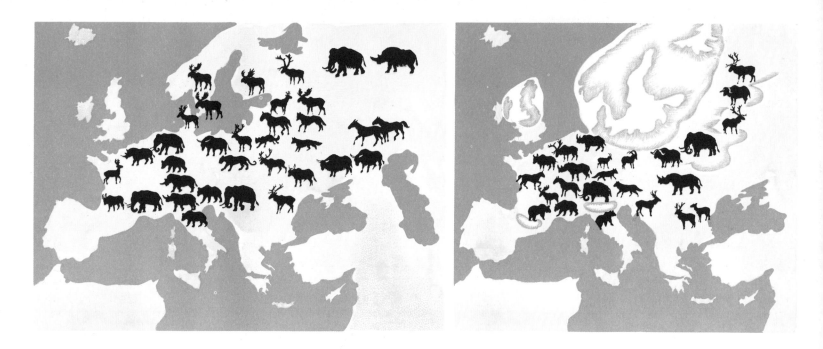

The climatic changes had a dramatic effect on the distribution of plants and animals. During the interglacials Europe was covered with lush vegetation and was teeming with life. The forests were made up of oak, beech, maple, ash and hazel. Animals of these warmer periods were the rhinoceros, straight-tusked elephant, and the lion.

With the onset of the colder periods the scene would gradually change. The tundra, with its mosses, lichens and stunted willows, as well as the coniferous forest belt, known as the taiga, would gradually edge southwards. The animals too would be different. Reindeer browsed on the sparse vegetation of the tundra. Other animals such as the woolly rhinoceros and the mammoth had thick shaggy coats to protect them from the intense cold.

The maps above show, on the left, the animals which lived in Europe during an interglacial period; and on the right, those of glacial times. Notice how much further south the mammoth and reindeer are during the advance of the ice.

The different types of plants and animals found as fossils help palaeontologists to date and correlate the various layers of rock. The dating and correlation of rocks which have originated during the ice age are most important in the study of human evolution.

What caused the ice to advance is not known with certainty, but the most likely reason is a variation in the quantity of solar radiation received on Earth. One thing which is known is that the Earth has had ice ages before and almost certainly will again.

LIFE IN THE ICE AGE

The prehistoric men who lived in Europe during the cold periods of the ice age had to cope with extreme hardship. The great ice cap which covered most of northern Europe caused freezing winds which brought blizzards and periods of severe cold. In the search for game the men would have crossed regions cave and seal up its entrance. Furs and tools were some of the hunter's most valued possessions and these, together with fire, allowed him to survive the harshness of the climate.

It was during this time that Neanderthal man (p.38) lived. The winter was particularly a period of testing

like the tundra of today. They would have had to travel far to the south to find the coniferous forests and grassy steppes. During the long winter, snow storms would howl and the temperature would drop to 40° C below zero in the northern and eastern parts of the ice cap. Game in these times served not only to provide food but pelts and furs as well. Rough clothes were made out of the skins which were also used to line the and severe hardship. Many of the group would die before the arrival of the milder weather of the spring. Their methods of trapping game required considerable skill and they used various tricks to ensnare their prey. Cave bear, various deer and the rhinoceros were all hunted. The men would have to work together and they were no doubt able to communicate well with each other.

Left: Amongst the most amazing discoveries of this period are those made at Drachenloch (Dragon's Hole), a cave 2,500 m. up in the Alps. Here were found the bones of cave-bears, mainly skulls, carefully lined up behind little walls of chalk pebbles. It has been assumed that this must have represented some sort of prehistoric hunting ceremony, some sort of cult of the bear. If this was so, then Drachenloch must be the most ancient sanctuary of man ever discovered. A similar discovery of rhinoceros skulls, placed in a circle, were found at Teschik-Tasch in southern Uzbeckistan, U.S.S.R. Other finds have been made in Austria and Germany.

Below: Neanderthal men hunted the cave bear. They had already acquired a considerable skill, for they did not use only brute force, but various tricks to capture their prey. Above the entry to the lairs of the cave bear they would make a pile of large stones. These would then be hurled down on the frightened animals when they came out. Face to face the cave bear would have been a formidable enemy for, when on its hind legs, it would have been a metre taller than Neanderthal man.

Below: One way of obtaining game was to drive the animals over a ledge or a deep cleft in the rock. In the latter case the weaker animals would fall to their death while the others would clear the jump. Such activities required a considerable degree of cooperation between the members of the hunting party. In the first instance the herd would have to be located, rounded up, and then driven towards the obstacle. Perhaps this was achieved by shouting or by the use of fire.

THE ORIGINAL CAVE MAN

When the first specimen of Neanderthal man was unearthed by workmen in 1856 it was the subject of a long and heated debate among the scientists of the day. Many refused to believe that here was an ancestor of modern man. They were influenced in their reasoning by the work of the famous eighteenth-century French naturalist Georges Cuvier (1769—1832) who had exclaimed that man does not exist in fossilised form. The discovery of more specimens of prehistoric man together with the writings of Charles Darwin (1809—1882) were to change the attitudes of the scientists.

The early descriptions of Neanderthal man were based on a specimen which in life had been crippled with arthritis. From this arose the idea that here was a sturdily built man who stooped and walked with a shuffle. He has become the original cave man of many cartoons.

In fact Neanderthal man was able to walk as well as we can. Although built more sturdily than most present-day people, and with massive ridges over the eyes, Neanderthal bore many resemblances to modern man. His brain was about the same size or larger than the average man of today.

Always living in danger, subjected to a harsh climate, hunger and frequent fights with large and wild animals, Neanderthal man had very little chance of reaching old age. The bones of a fifty year old man already showed every sign of old age. Most men died well before fifty. Forty per cent of the skeletons discovered belong to individuals less than twenty years old and forty per cent of the remainder to persons between twenty and thirty years old.

Neanderthal man is usually considered to be a subspecies of modern man, being given the scientific name *Homo sapiens neanderthalensis.* His line of evolution from the older forms of man is not yet fully known, but certainly about 35,000 to 40,000 years ago Neanderthal man disappeared from the Earth and was replaced by a new more advanced form of man, little different from the men of today.

Above: Neanderthal man's skill as a hunter is not doubted. He used many ways of capturing and killing the animals which he needed for his survival. Pits might be dug on the tracks of animals. Others could be sited so that the animals could be driven in to them. The pit would have been covered with twigs and branches. The bottom may have been suitably treated to wound or kill the beast. All of these activities required a great deal of cooperation between the individuals involved.

Right: This picture shows the Neander valley which lies between the towns of Düsseldorf and Elberfeld, in West Germany. In 1856 workers discovered a skull cap in a quarry, which Carl Fuhlrott (centre) asked to have for examination. He presented the remains of Neanderthal man to the world at a naturalists congress in Bonn, in 1857. Neither the fossilised man nor his discovery received a favourable welcome. The map shows the location of the finds of Neanderthal man.

THE LIFE OF NEANDERTHAL MAN

While naturalists were arguing about the significance of the discovery of Neanderthal man they really knew that the only way to settle the argument was to find more specimens. If the skeleton was nothing more than a modern man with deformities, caused by a succession of illnesses, another one would not be found. A single further find, showing the same extraordinary features would solve the problem once and for all. This discovery was in fact made in Belgium, in

physically from modern man but who were able to think and manufacture tools and who had also been alive in the ice age. Over the following decades more and more discoveries were made of Neanderthal man and from these we can piece together their appearance and their way of life. The average volume of their brain was almost the same as, or even superior to, that of modern man.

Neanderthal man was considerably more advanced

1886, when a bed yielded two skeletons both of which were identical to the find in the Neanderthal valley.

Although other finds had been made in the intervening years nothing was to prove the case of the existence of Neanderthal man so well as the remains from the Spy Cave, in Namur, Belgium. Beside the human remains various flint tools and a number of bones belonging to long extinct animals were also unearthed. Here therefore was proof that these implements belonged to individuals who were different

than *Homo erectus*. He was able to think and to act upon his thoughts and could therefore overcome some of life's difficulties. The weapons and tools are proof of the development of his mental faculties. He made the tools from flint, or quartzite. Normally they were worked to a spearhead or point, but triangle shapes were common too. Various knives and scrapers were made as well. From the discoveries which have been made we can assume that wooden clubs and sharpened sticks would also have been used.

Below: In 1908 the discovery at Le Moustier of the grave of a young Neanderthal man was greeted with surprise. His head was resting on his right forearm, his left hand was stretched forward, and flint implements and charred animal bones surrounded the skeleton as if they were offerings. This young man had been buried. His companions had gone to considerable trouble to dig a grave. This burial, recognised as the earliest in history, shows that these men were already attached to each other by human-like sentiments. Perhaps they had their own law by which one of them could order the others to bury a dead companion. The way that this particular boy had been laid suggests that death was regarded as a form of sleep. Other similar burials have been found in Russia.

Above: The culture of Neanderthal man is called Mousterian. It is named after Le Moustier, near Peyzac in France. As in the case of most prehistoric cultures the commonest items remaining are the flint tools. Most of the implements are flakes. These are made from chips off the main lump of flint. Side scrapers and triangular points are common and were used for cutting up and skinning animals. Wooden spears were also a common weapon.

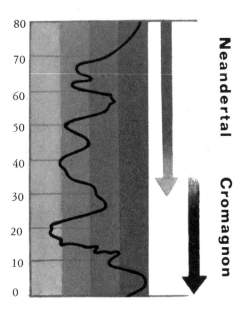

Above: An early way of communicating might have been by the use of signs. The examples shown here are used by a present-day tribe in Botswana and mean, left to right, antelope, porcupine, and lion.

Right: The graph shows the effect of the movement of the icecap on the temperature. Neanderthal man gave way, in Europe, to a new type of man: Cro-Magnon man. The bands, left to right, indicate warm, temperate, cold, and very cold climates. The divisions, bottom to top, are in tens of thousands of years.

Neandertal

Cromagnon

NEANDERTHAL MAN IN THE MIDDLE EAST

For many years the majority of specimens of Neanderthal man were found in Europe. It was only when specimens were found in the Middle East that it was realised that there were two types. It is far from easy to work out the relationship between these types and to understand just how they fit into the evolutionary line which leads to modern man.

Neanderthal man of western Europe has become known as the classic neanderthaler while the others are considered progressive. This is not to imply that there are not similarities between the two types for

there are. In general, however, the features of the progressive form are not so extreme.

One theory is that the Neanderthal remains at Ehringsdorf in Germany and Saccopastore in Italy were descended from Steinheim man. As evolution took its course a separate line developed. This line, because of the harshness of the European climate became specialised to living in a cold climate. The most important changes in man would have occurred in the more favourable areas and this is why the discoveries in the Middle East are so important.

Above: The finds from two caves in Israel are very important. The oldest cave is Tabūn from which specimens have been found resembling the classic Neanderthal form.
However they have features which link with other finds in Africa. The other cave, Skūhl, has a form resembling the classic Neanderthal man but with features which are reminiscent of modern man. Perhaps it was the descendants of these men which were later to arrive in Europe.

Left: The hunters who began to leave the Middle East for Europe some 50,000 years ago already had many of the characteristics of modern man. Shown are the hunter of an earlier period discovered at Předmostí in Czechoslovakia (top) and the hunter discovered at Cro-Magnon in France (bottom) who gave the name to a group of people.

Right: Charles Darwin, author of two of the most important books in natural history. *On the Origin of Species by Means of Natural Selection* was first published in 1859, while the *Descent of Man* was issued in 1871. He was educated at the universities of Edinburgh and Cambridge. Darwin joined the naval vessel *Beagle* at the age of twenty-two.

Above: During the voyage of the H.M.S. *Beagle,* Charles Darwin collected a large amount of information about plants and animals. This vast store of data was to be invaluable to him in explaining the mechanism of evolution. When Darwin returned to England further reading and research eventually led to the theory of evolution by means of natural selection. Plants and animals reproduce rapidly, which means that there is a constant fight for survival. Only those which exhibit features most advantageous to their environment will succeed. This was later to be called 'the survival of the fittest'.

INTELLIGENT MAN — *Homo sapiens sapiens*

The first fossils that could be said to be truly human and almost identical with modern man have been dated about 50,000 years old, although the original find, known as Cro-Magnon man, is about 30,000—20,000 years old.

In 1868 a railway line was being constructed in the valley of the River Vézere near Les Eyzies in the Dordogne region of France. While excavating a limestone cliff the engineers uncovered a rock shelter in which they found contained five adult skeletons. These people had been carefully buried together with weapons and bone jewellery which were placed beside them. One of the skeletons was that of an adult male of about fifty years of age. He became known as the 'old man' of Cro-Magnon. He was tall, between 170 and 180 cm, with an athletic build. His brain had reached the same capacity as that of modern man.

As we can see there is little difference physically between Cro-Magnon man and his twentieth century counterpart. So why did Cro-Magnon man live in a cave and hunt his food while we live in centrally heated houses and buy our food in shops? The difference is of course due to the layers of 'civilisation' with which we have become surrounded.

Now that he had acquired a large brain, the adaptive nature of man was directed towards increasing his ability as a hunter, protecting himself from the weather, improving his co-operation with other members of his tribe, and trying to understand the world in which he lived. Things that he was not able to understand would be attributed to the actions of a god or gods. We have direct evidence of major advances made, including the introduction of agriculture, improving the techniques of stone use and the discovery and use of metals. We can only guess at the use of language, as early man was not able to leave any record until he could write. It is then that we leave prehistory and enter the history itself.

Above: Prehistoric man at this time was already an able hunter. Armed with sturdy wooden spears with sharp flint heads bound to them, flint daggers and powerful clubs, he was no longer confined to hunting small game. He was now able to stalk and kill animals as large as a mammoth. One individual obviously would not have been able to do this but for a group united by language it would have been possible. Together they could act as one creature with many arms and legs and with dozens of spears. Man was also able to draw on his intelligence and the accumulated experience of the whole tribe.

Left: The pictures are prehistoric cave paintings showing a round trap and a mammoth caught in one. These traps were deep pits placed on a path frequented by the animals and hidden with grass and leaves. Once an animal had fallen into the pit it could easily be killed by the group. This shows the increasing ingenuity of man in outwitting large animals and killing them for food.

Right: These are hands of people of the Stone Age. When scientists write of industries and cultures they mean the products of a single group and a whole society. Often all that we have to represent these activities are the stone tools. As man became more expert in handling stone he learnt how to strike it in the correct place to produce a greater variety of tools which were both sharper and lighter. Heads for spears, delicate arrow heads, and tools for scraping and for boring holes in bone all became part of man's tool kit.

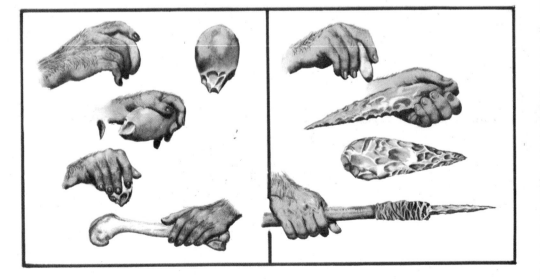

MAGIC HUNTING RITES

Existence in the Stone Age depended on the ability of the group to kill animals for food and skins, and on the collection of plants, berries, roots and fruits. The result of failure was starvation.

We all know how superstitious fishermen can be; how they will use only one type of lure or bait and wear only certain clothing. Prehistoric man was no different. Although we have no evidence that he had man-like figures. The very act of drawing the animal had considerable significance, but from parallels drawn with Australian aboriginal art some active part may have been played by the tribe as a whole. Before a hunt the males could have congregated in front of the painting of the animal they were hoping to hunt the next day. This would have given the leader the chance to act out his strategy and to allocate roles to

a favourite spear or dagger, we do know that he carried out pre-hunting rites to ensure success in the hunt. It is thought that cave art, although perhaps not originally executed for magical purposes, became part of ceremonies. The vast majority of this art shows mammoths, deer, ibex, birds, fish and snakes being hunted. The animals are shown with wounds in their sides, caught in traps, and on occasions being killed by humans. the other hunters. This may have been the origin of a witch doctor-like figure. Symbolically masked dancing men may have been portrayed, the mask often being of an animal. A particularly fine example of a man wearing a horned bison mask has been found in France. These dancing and miming rites may have developed into initiation ceremonies to admit young men in to the hunting group within the tribe.

46

Above: In a cave near Montespan in the south of France archaeologists found on the floor a bear modelled in clay. The bear does not have a head and its body is pierced with holes, the marks of prehistoric javelins. We can almost see the prehistoric hunters performing dances and ceremonies in front of this statue. They could even have fixed a real bear's head and perhaps a skin to their fetish and then hurled spears at it. Certainly very powerful magic would have been needed before hunting this dangerous animal.

Above: The cave bear lived at the same time as prehistoric man. This enormous animal was very dangerous to hunt, nevertheless man still attacked it. We can tell this by the discovery of a bear's head which had received a serious wound from a hunter which had later healed. A fragment of the stone point was embedded in the wound, and remained in the bone until the animal died.

Above: On the site of Dolní Věstonice in Czechoslovakia which was used by the mammoth hunters, small figurines of animals have been found. These have had their legs broken off and may have been used in magic hunting rites.

CAVE PAINTINGS

In 1880, at the Lisbon Congress of Prehistory, Don Marcelino de Sautuola, a Spanish amateur historian, presented a sensational paper in which he told of the discoveries he had made in a cave at Altamira in Spain, where there are paintings depicting many animals, some of which are now extinct. His claims were rejected by scientists and dismissed as the wanderings of an eccentric mind. Over twenty years later two scientists, E. Cartailhac and H. Breuil, went to the cave to examine it in detail. 'We have just found a marvellous, unknown world,' wrote Breuil. Altamira proved to be the first of many galleries of cave paintings to be discovered. The most recent to be found is the Capov cave, by the Ural River in the U.S.S.R.

There appears to have been two main periods of cave art and these are related to definite cultures. The cultures of prehistoric man are named after their place of discovery. The culture of the Neanderthals is called Mousterian after Le Moustier, France; that of Cro-Magnon, Aurignacian (Aurignac, Toulouse, France). This was followed by the Gravettian (La Gravette, France, 20,000—26,000 B.C.); Soultrean (Soultré, France, 15,000—20,000 B.C.); and the Magdalenian (La Madeleine, France, 10,000—15,000 B.C.). It is difficult to know if cave art started in the late Aurignacian or early Gravettian periods but it was certainly a major activity during the latter period. France was the main centre.

The early form was not linked with hunting and very few wounded animals or weapons were drawn. These paintings, which are quite often near the mouths of the caves, may have been painted just for the sake of representing animals and life. In time the significance of the art form changed. It retreated back into the darkness of the cave, and its meaning into the dark superstitious nature of mankind.

Above: For his paints the prehistoric artist used mineral pigments and coloured earths, grinding them into powder and mixing them with water and animal fat. The paintings are well preserved because of the even temperature (about 8 °C) and the low humidity of the caves. Cave art is widely distributed in Europe but it naturally depended on the availability of suitable caves. In France it occurs south of the river Loire and west of the Rhône. In Spain the main finds have been in the Cantabrian mountains and there have been scattered finds elsewhere. Recent discoveries have been made in Russia, 4,000 km. from the main centre of cave art in France.

Below: In one cave the first paintings were found 500 m. from the entrance and the last, far from the light of day, over 1,000 m. into the cave. To paint under these conditions the artist would have had to use a lamp similar to the one shown here, found in the famous cave of Lascaux, in France.

Below: This colourful bison is from the great painted ceiling of the Altamira cave. It was rediscovered by a five year old girl, Maria. She found it while playing in a small side chamber so as not to disturb her father who was excavating in the main chamber of the cave.

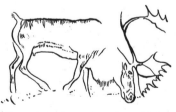

Above left: A reindeer from Kaiserloch.
Above right: A hind from Les Eyzies.
Left: A mare from Lascaux
The artists painted these pictures over a period of 12,000 years and then suddenly stopped 10,000 years ago. At the same time the Magdalenian culture also disappears. This change coincided with the end of the last glaciation and the movement of the reindeer herds northwards. Did this painter and hunter move with the reindeer and perhaps find no suitable caves in which to express his artistic abilities? From the few illustrations shown it is clear that the technique and artistry of Stone Age man were of an exceptionally high order. It does not seem possible that such fine work could be produced in the flickering light of a poor lamp, with a finger for a brush and earth for paint.

THE VENUS FIGURES

mammoth ivory and bone, limestone, sandstone, coal, and from clay baked in a fire.

With very few exceptions these figures are found within the areas of the Gravettian culture. The human figures are all females, grossly distorted, with exaggerated breasts, buttocks and thighs. They are invariably pregnant, with a much reduced head that has no features.

Wherever they are found, from the River Don to the Pyrénées Mountains, they all have the same basic style. What was their function? It is thought that these small figures, few were over 15 cm. high, portrayed the importance of the female in the hunter society. Without women there could be no new life, there could be no tribe. Woman was therefore the source of life, but not only this; she collected and cooked the food and cared for the children. She was a symbol of the vital fruitfulness that the tribe and the animals and plants they ate needed to survive. Without this life force there could be no plants, no animals and no tribe.

It is also not surprising that when these figures were found by modern man that he should call them Venus figures and think of them as fertility symbols.

It has been suggested that this type of symbolism could have led to the matriarchal system (in which the female is dominant) that lasted for many thousands of years. Relationship in this system is inherited through the female. In fact it may have been this system that gave rise to the clan, where a single female ancestor is worshipped.

At the same time as cave art was flourishing in France, prehistoric man was carving a wide range of materials.

Many products have been found, delicately carved with intricate patterns and designs. However, the most outstanding works are those of animals and women made out of a wide range of substances including

Left: Ceremonies might have been connected with the Venus statuettes. They could have been worshipped and asked to provide the group with lots of children and to help the tribe in its hunting. These ceremonies could have been conducted by a 'head man', a figure similar to that portrayed in the cave paintings.

Left: A hunter at Předmostí, Czechoslovakia, scratched a Venus on a piece of mammoth tusk. The outline of this woman is made of geometric shapes.

Below: It is very unusual to find faces depicted in either the cave or carved art forms. Here are two human faces that have come to us from more than 10,000 years: the face of a young girl found at Brassempouy in France and a face from Věstonice, Czechoslovakia.

THE MYSTERY OF DEATH

living. There in front of them was someone else, a mysterious silent stranger.

Prehistoric men saw death all around them. They were after all hunters, who lived by killing game. Even so, they may not have looked on their own death as a law of nature that could not be avoided. In fact even after the funeral rites, they might dream of talking to the dead. And when the dead came to them in these dreams, they would sit around the fire, recalling past hunts and old legends.

The imagination of prehistoric man probably still confused reality with fantasy and superstition. He may not have known how to tell the difference between life and death. It was a small step from this to believing that the dead only went away somewhere, and came back from time to time.

The way to the land of death was evidently a long one, and that is why the dead were so well equipped, being given clothes, weapons, jewellery, talismans and food. Amongst the many graveyards of this period there is the interesting discovery of the two children buried in a cave near Menton in the south of France. As a last token of affection, those who loved them placed necklaces in their tomb, and magnificent belts sewn with thousands of tiny sea shells. Most of the burials were single, and no attempt was made to separate the living from the dead, the bodies often being buried in the refuse of the cave floor.

The earliest burials are of Neanderthal people, for example at Monte Circeo in Italy and La Chapelle aux Saints in France.

When death came to a member of a band of hunters, it must have made a powerful impression on the others. It must have been a great mystery to them. A healthy strong man, perhaps even the healthiest and strongest man in the group, suddenly became powerless; he stopped breathing and his heart stopped beating. Death came, breaking all connections with the

Above: When the dead man was well provided for on his long journey, the hunters would cover his head, and sometimes his whole body with red ochre. The red tombs of Cro-Magnon men are spread all over Europe. Some have been discovered, but others remain hidden, and for all we know every day we could be walking over the ground covering such a tomb. We do not know why red ochre played such an important part in the funeral rites. Perhaps red was symbolic because it is the same colour as blood, which is the essence of life itself. This practice of providing for the dead occurs even with the advanced civilisations: the Egyptians buried their Pharaohs with food and gold for the afterlife.

Left: At Tuc d'Audoubert in France there is a cave that contains two sculptured bisons. Around these, footprints have been traced — perhaps those of dancing youngsters. Could it be that this is the place where a tribe of Cro-Magnon hunters carried out their initiation ceremonies? If so, this would have been to ensure that the next generation would have its fair share of good hunters, and mothers of fine healthy children.

THE HUMAN HAND

One of the most fascinating of all the cave paintings is the print of a human hand at the Gargas cave, in the Pyrénées, between Aventignan and St. Bertrand de Comminges. Over many thousands of years this hand

thumb would have allowed the animal to isolate objects from its surroundings: to examine them more closely by smell, sight, and touch. The next step would have been the freeing of the hands from locomotive

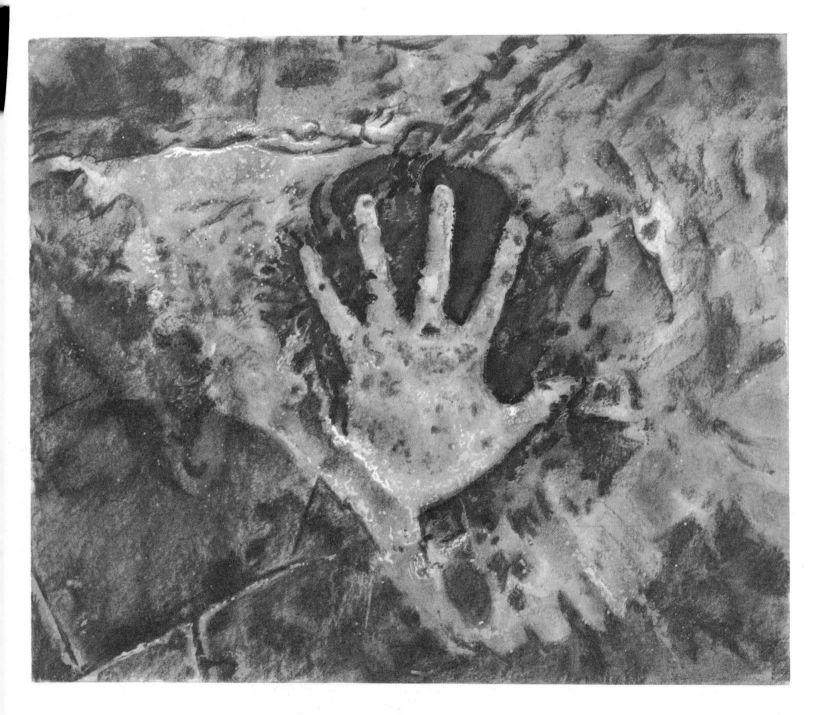

seems to be stretcned out in a silent gesture of greeting to us his distant descendants.

The human hand is a remarkable precision instrument unique in the animal world; it has evolved in two stages. The first is the opposable thumb (p. 55) evolved by the primates for holding branches. This

duties when man started to walk on two legs. Then tool use and later tool making could occur. The size of the brain, to give coordination, would have been important, and from the fossil evidence it would seem that the evolution of the hand and brain have been inter-dependent.

Above: We know that as man's hand evolved so did his ability to make more sophisticated tools and weapons. The australopithecines, like the chimpanzee of today, were able to clumsily wield clubs. As control of the hand improved these became the more accurate and lethal spears of early Stone Age man. When the hand could function like that of present-day man it became possible to throw these spears, like arrows coming from a bow. This greater range and accuracy allowed man to hunt swifter, larger animals, like the reindeer, with a much greater chance of success.

Above: Top to bottom, *Homo erectus,* Neanderthal man, modern man. The progressive evolution of the skull is very clear. We can see how the change in diet reduced the teeth, the size of the jaw, and made the front of the face flatter. We can see how the dome of the skull became rounder and the forehead moved forward to allow for the increase in the size of the brain.

Above: The hand of man allows what anthropologists call 'the perfect opposition of thumb and index finger'. Notice how this differs from the hand of the chimpanzee (left) and the gorilla.

Below: These paintings at the Khoit-Tsenger Agoui cave in Mongolia portray, from left to right, a goat, camel, ostrich, and a bull.

Above: Women and girls would have needed sensitive and deft hands to scrape skins and to sew clothes and shoes from skin and furs. They would also have threaded shells and beads on to gut for decoration. Many different sorts of needle have been found dating back 16—17,000 years.

MAN ADORNS HIMSELF

Fire was an inseparable companion of Cro-Magnon man. He no longer relied on chance to obtain it; he knew how to kindle it for himself using flint and pieces of iron ore. The hunters would bring the game they had killed to the fire in order to cook the meat on flat stones, or else to place it in the glowing coals and hot ashes. Near the fire they would make their weapons from flint and bone, using large flat stones as tables. There, too, animal bones would be made into fine buckles for fur garments; into spikes, needles, daggers and harpoons. But they were also made into objects that were not of a strictly practical value. Necklaces and bracelets would be made out of the teeth of animals. Pearly sea-shells and many other objects were also used.

While excavations were being carried out near Mainz in Germany a workshop for making necklaces was discovered. Rocks served as workbenches and mixed with the flint tools were many shells with their tops cut off. In other excavations necklaces made of fossils have been found. The less the hunters could account for their strange shape and mysterious origin the more magical they may have believed them to be. Men, women and children adorned themselves. Perhaps some of them thought their necklaces and other adornments as giving protection against accident and sickness.

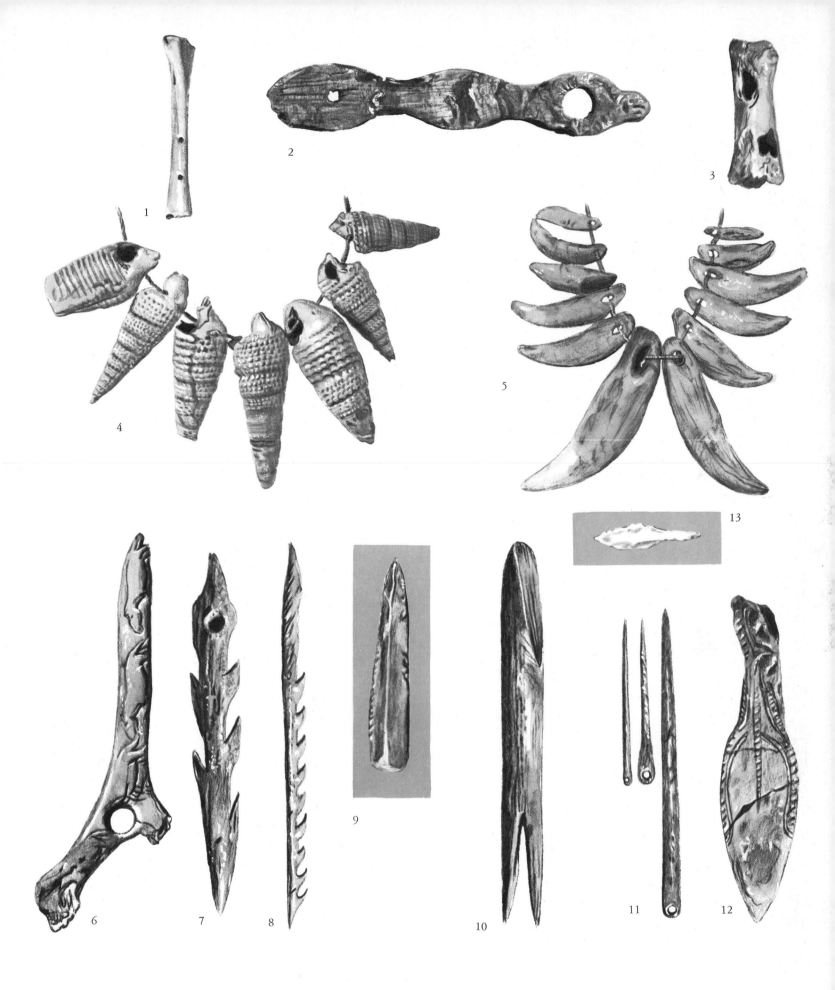

Wild animals not only provided meat and skins, but also bones from which were fashioned implements and weapons.

The illustrations show:

1. Flute, with carefully worked holes, 2. Clasp for a tur garment, 3. Whistle made from reindeer bone, 4. Necklace of shells, 5. Necklace of wolf and fox teeth, 6. Staff engraved with wild animals, 7. & 8. Bone harpoons, 9. Flint knife, 10. Scraper made of bone, 11. Needles, 12. Shovel, 13. Flint tool.

MAN BUILDS A HOUSE

A group of hunters probably consisted of up to fifteen to twenty people including the children. They lived communally; all participated in the search for food and shelter; and all kept watch for the group's safety. In the open air they would camp on slopes that faced south, in the lee of the north wind. There would have to be water nearby, and a good view from the camp over the surrounding countryside, so that they

however, there were no caves, and the reindeer hunters made themselves ingenious underground shelters, of which the upper walls and roof were made of wood and animal bones, covered with tough layers of skin. Similar people in Germany and Denmark erected a complicated double shelter. Inside one tent dwelling they would put up another smaller one, where they probably slept at night, spending the day in the larger

could watch the movements of the herds of game. To protect themselves from the cold at night, and from the bad weather, they made shelters which were like tents made out of pelts and furs. In winter it was worse: the weather was harsh and cruel, and the prehistoric hunter had to shelter himself as best he could.

In western Europe the huntsmen often made use of overhanging rocks and entrances to caves in which to make their homes. On the steppes of the Ukraine,

outer tent, where the fire was situated. With the coming of agriculture this temporary accommodation could be replaced with a permanent structure made from wood and mud and thus the first towns and cities were created.

Man now had made his own environment as protection against bad weather and in this first human dwelling he worked, talked, and rested, keeping both the cold and darkness at bay.

Above: To survive, the prehistoric hunting group, and its later larger descendant the tribe, had to have a well organised social structure. At this stage in the evolution of human society delegation of work between males and females had already taken place. Women would have collected berries, fetched water, cooked the food, and looked after the children while the men hunted. There was probably an expert hunter who would have led the group on its expeditions and may also have directed the movement of the tribe in its search for new hunting grounds. The expert hunter may therefore have gradually risen to the position of a chief, and as his eldest son would have been carefully taught by him the position could have become hereditary. The masked figure found in many cave paintings could have been the same individual and so he could have held a position between priest and king. No doubt other work evolved in a similar way: an expert in house building would be called upon more and more to build houses until it became a full-time occupation.

Left: On the steppes of Eastern Europe there was very little material of use for building shelters. Most houses would have been built from animal bones and skins, an example of this type of building is shown.

Right: When evening came and the day's work was finished the group probably gathered around the fire and listened to the old men telling tales of hunting and deeds of valour of their ancestors. This may have been the way in which our ancient legends were created. These men would have become the keepers of the tribe's history.

THE FIRST FARMERS

Thousands of years have passed. The great ice cap has slowly retreated to the north, as far as the mountains of northern Scandinavia. We are now in the long, wet spring of the post-glacial period. The appearance of the European landscape and the type of animals have once again changed. In this period, about 10,000 years ago, man is still a hunter, but now he hunts small game and fishes in the many rivers and lakes.

vegetables. He crushed and ground the seed into a coarse flour, which gave him the taste of bread for the first time. He domesticated animals, becoming a herdsman. If meat was needed there was no longer the need to hunt.

The distribution of wild wheat, sheep and goats indicate that agriculture started in the Middle East. The change was a gradual one. Starting in the Middle East,

For the first time he is accompanied on his hunting trips by a new friend, the dog, the first animal he tamed.

After some four thousand more years, hunting as a mode of living slowly gave way to farming. This is such an important turning point in the history of man that it is called the Neolithic period (New Stone Age) and the process that caused it the Neolithic Revolution. The appearance of farming marks a new period in human history. Man no longer took advantage of nature's gifts, but cultivated them by his own hard work, taking the harvest as the reward for his effort. The first farmers broke up the soil with a primitive pick, and then planted corn, barley, millet, and various

the idea of farming spread to eastern Europe in about 6,500 B.C., arrived in central Europe by 5,000 B.C., and most likely did not reach Britain until about 4,000 B.C.

Farming on the North American continent was an independent discovery and maize may have been grown before wheat was in the Old World. With this new method of obtaining his food man's life became more secure; with food stored for the winter he could turn his mind to other things. He was now able to start improving his way of life. Soon we see the first containers made of baked ochre; the first materials woven on a primitive loom; and a greater variety of implements and tools.

Above: Not everyone changed to farming. Those whose land was unsuitable or who could obtain sufficient food by hunting maintained their old way of life. This is particularly true of people like the Eskimos who still fish, hunt, and use stone-tipped arrows to shoot migratory birds.

Above: From excavations in the Dordogne, it has been possible to find out the type of animals man hunted for tens of thousands of years. Those which were hunted are coloured and the rest have been left in black and white.

Right: A human footprint from the Cabreets Cave in France and man's first footprint on the moon. These two are only separated by 15,000 years. This may seem a very long time, but when compared with the millions of years which have passed since *Ramapithecus* lived it is a very small span. If we traced our family trees, through our fathers, grandfathers, great-grandfathers, and so on, we should have to go back less than a thousand generations to reach our ancestor who left his footprint in the cave. Man's achievements since then have been immense in agriculture, writing, art, and science. We can only wonder at what the next 15,000 years may bring.

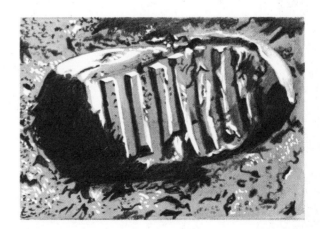

Left: The first stage in the cultivation of crops was to make a suitable clearance in the forest. To do this axes like the one in the picture were used and were very efficient.

61

Index

Page numbers in **bold** type refer to illustrations

47
35
—
12